Science Project

by Jane A C West

Illustrated by Peter Richardson

FULL FLIGHT

Titles in the Full Flight Thrills and Spills series:

The Knight Olympics	Jonny Zucker
Pied Piper of London	Danny Pearson
The Science Project	Jane A C West
Gorilla Thriller	Richard Taylor
Clone Zone	Jillian Powell
Clowning Around	Helen Orme
Time to go Home	David Orme
Haunted Car	Roger Hurn
Dinosaur Rampage	Craig Allen
Rubbish Ghost	Jillian Powell

Badger Publishing Limited
Oldmedow Road, Hardwick Industrial Estate,
King's Lynn PE30 4JJ
Telephone: 01438 791 037
www.badgerlearning.co.uk

2 4 6 8 10 9 7 5 3

The Science Project ISBN 978-1-84926-981-0

Text © Jane A C West 2013
Complete work © Badger Publishing Limited 2013
Second edition © 2016

Publisher: Susan Ross
Senior Editor: Danny Pearson
Designer: Fiona Grant
Illustrator: Peter Richardson

Contents

New words:

scowled	experiment
blotting paper	imagined
copper	promised
zinc	surprised
discovery	nervous

Main characters:

Jilly

Ben

Mr Z

Chapter 1

Best Friends (Not!)

"Right," said Mr Jones. "Today we start our new science project. I want you to work in pairs. Jilly and Ben, Parva and Rowan…"

Jilly groaned. Across the classroom, Ben scowled. Mr Jones sighed and shook his head.

"Ben's so silly!" said Jilly to her friend Nina. "I wish I didn't have to work with him."

"Jilly's so bossy!" said Ben to his friend Luka. "I wish I didn't have to work with her."

"They'll be a good team," said Mr Jones to himself. "When they realise they could get on if they tried."

Ben was sulking. Jilly looked fed up. "What are we going to do our project on?" she said.

Ben shrugged.

Jilly sighed. "What about using wet blotting paper to separate out the colours of ink?" she said.

"Boring!" said Ben.

Jilly imagined pouring ink over Ben's head and watching the different colours. "What about making a machine to find out which cheese is the smelliest?" said Jilly.

"Boring!" moaned Ben.

Jilly imagined getting a really smelly cheese and stuffing it up Ben's nostrils. "What about making a battery for a light bulb using a lemon?" said Jilly, crossly.

"Huh?" said Ben.

"It's an interesting experiment," said
Jilly. She was really fed up now.
Ben was so annoying. Really annoying.
Really, really annoying.

"A lemon? Are you pulling my leg?"
asked Ben.

Jilly imagined pulling Ben's leg as she
dragged him around the playground in
the mud. The thought made her smile.
Maybe she could borrow a horse and
pull Ben through a hedge backwards.
And in the mud.

"Haven't you got any *good* ideas?"
said Ben.

"Yes!" shouted Jilly. "NOT WORKING
WITH YOU!"

She walked away, her back stiff with anger.

Ben rolled his eyes. "Girls!" They just didn't have a sense of humour.

Chapter 2
Go Team!

Mr Jones made Ben say sorry.
Mr Jones made Jilly promise to work
with Ben. Mr Jones promised himself
three bars of chocolate and a pizza
when he got home.

Being a teacher was hard work. Maybe
he had better make it four bars of
chocolate… and two pizzas.

"We'll do the light bulb thing," said
Ben. He rolled his eyes.

Jilly imagined Ben's eyes rolling along
the table and dropping onto the floor.

She imagined the squelching sound they'd make when she squished them with her foot. Two squelches for two eyeballs.

Jilly looked at her shopping list. She thought she had everything. This is what she read:

A lemon
A grapefruit
An orange
A lime
A potato
One copper nail
One zinc screw
Wire
A small light bulb.

She bought everything on the list for her experiment. Then she thought about Ben. No. She really didn't need him!

Ben looked for the shopping list Jilly had given him of the things he needed for his experiment. He'd lost it. Oh, well. He bought:

A bottle of lemonade
A parsnip
A magnet
A screwdriver
One packet of crisps
A candle.

The crisps were for himself, obviously.

That seemed about right. Ben was pleased with himself.

He was pretty sure he'd remembered everything on Jilly's list. And if he hadn't, he didn't care anyway. She was really annoying. Really, really annoying.

This is what Jilly said when she saw what Ben had bought: "You are such an idiot!"

This is what Ben did: he rolled his eyes. But, unfortunately for Jilly, they didn't roll on the floor, so Jilly couldn't make them squelch. Ben was really annoying.

Chapter 3

As Good as Gold

Jilly's experiment worked really well. It was her experiment. It definitely wasn't Ben's experiment. He was so annoying.

Jilly made a battery using the lemon, nail, screw and wire. The little light bulb glowed brightly.

"That's pretty cool," said Ben.
He looked very surprised. He had not
thought Jilly's experiment would work.

"Thanks!" said Jilly. She was even more
surprised. Mostly because Ben was
being nice. But also because her
experiment had worked. Those sorts of
surprises were pretty good.

"Do you want some lemonade?" asked
Ben.

"Oh, thanks!" said Jilly. She was still
surprised.

"Have some of my crisps, too," said
Ben. He didn't usually share his crisps
with anyone. Maybe Jilly wasn't so bad
after all.

"Thanks," said Jilly. "Do you want to make a battery using the grapefruit?"

"Cool!" said Ben.

The little light bulb glowed brightly. They were both really pleased with themselves.

"I'm going to tell Mr Jones that we've made a battery," said Jilly. "He won't believe it!"

While she was gone, Ben decided to add his parsnip, lemonade, magnet and candle to the battery. He was sure it would make a super-size battery. That would be amazing. But nothing could have prepared him for...

KER-POW!

Smoke filled the science lab.

"Oops!" said Ben. "That was a surprise!"

Jilly came hurrying back. "What happened?" she asked.

"Er… I thought I'd experiment with the experiment," said Ben.

"You are such an idiot!" shouted Jilly. "Hang on a minute… what's that?"

"I don't know," said Ben. He peered through the smoke. "Something has happened to your grapefruit."

"Let me see," said Jilly, pushing him out of the way.

"Wow!" said Jilly.

"What's happened?" asked Ben.

"Wow!" said Jilly again.

"What's happened?" asked Ben again.

"It's not a grapefruit anymore,"
said Jilly.

"What's happened?" said Ben, crossly.

Jilly looked up at Ben. "It's not a
grapefruit… it looks like it's solid gold!"

Chapter 4

I Spy

"We're rich!" yelled Ben.

"Wow!" screamed Jilly.

"I'm going to buy an X-box…" said Ben, "and a Y-box… and a Z-box… and…"

"This is a really important experiment," said Jilly. "Everyone will be so amazed. We'll be famous! People will write books about our amazing discovery!"

"And new trainers… and a new bike… and…"

"Ben!" shouted Jilly. "It's even better than that! We'll get an 'A' on our science project!"

"You are such an idiot," said Ben. But he said it really quietly so Jilly couldn't hear him.

Later that evening, Jilly posted a message on the internet. It said that their school science experiment had found a way of turning things into gold. She was sure they'd get an 'A' on their project.

Jilly had the gold hidden in her school bag while they decided what to do with it.

Far away, a man with sunglasses, a false beard, and a hat like a spy was reading the internet. Then he took off his sunglasses so he could see what he was reading.

"Gold!" he said. "A way to turn things into gold! At last!"

Mr Z (which wasn't his real name) got in his car. It had tinted windows like a spy car. Then he put on his sunglasses so no one would recognise him.

He then put on the car headlights so he could see where he was going. The sunglasses and tinted windows made it a bit difficult to see anything...

Then he drove to Jilly and Ben's school.

Mr Z was going to steal the secret of how to turn things into gold. And then… he was going to be very, very rich.

Chapter 5

A to Z

Mr Z crawled along the corridor to the science lab. Several children tripped over Mr Z. What was this crazy, small man in sunglasses doing in school?

Then he took off his spy sunglasses so he could see where he was going. Oh. He was in the gym, not the lab.

He crawled back down the corridor until he found the lab. "Now I will steal the secret of turning things into gold!" he said.

Jilly walked into the science lab. She placed the gold grapefruit on her desk.

She saw Mr Z crawling on the floor. "Who are you?" she asked. "And why are you crawling on the floor of our school lab?"

"My name is… er… Mr Y," said Mr Z.

"Why?" asked Jilly.

"Yes. Y," said Mr Z.

"Oh," said Jilly. She was very puzzled.

"Are you the one who turned a grapefruit into gold?" asked Z.

"Yes!" said Jilly proudly. "Me and my fr... er... him!"

She pointed at Ben who had just walked into the room.

"Tell me the secret!" shouted Mr Z. "Or else!"

"Or else what?" asked Ben.

"Er... or else... something really bad will happen!" said Z.

"Never," said Ben.

"Run!" shouted Jilly.

"Never!" shouted Ben.

Then he threw a parsnip at Z. Then he threw a potato at Z. Then he threw every piece of fruit at Z and the empty bottle of lemonade. "You're really starting to annoy me!" Ben yelled at Z.

Ben did not realise he had picked up the golden grapefruit and had thrown that, too.

Mr Z had had enough. He never had liked being at school. He liked it even less now. So he put on his sunglasses and crawled away as fast as he could.

Mr Jones saw him go. "Who was that?" he asked Jilly.

"A spy who wanted to steal our secret!" she said.

"What secret?" asked Mr Jones.

"How to turn things into gold,"
said Ben.

"Really?" said Mr Jones. "That's a
surprise. How did you do it?"

"Ask Ben," said Jilly. "He's the one who
did it."

"Er… I don't really remember how
it happened," said Ben, looking a bit
nervous. "I just sort of made it up.
And… er… I forgot to write it down."

"I don't believe it. You are such an
idiot," said Jilly.

"You are so bossy," said Ben.

Mr Jones put his head in hands.

"By the way," said Jilly, "did we get
an 'A'?"

Nobody saw that the solid gold
grapefruit had rolled under the
bookcase.

Making a Fruit Battery

Yes, this experiment really does work!

You need:

A citrus fruit (lemon, lime, orange or grapefruit)

A copper nail, screw, or piece of wire, 5cm long

A zinc nail, screw or piece of wire, 5cm long

A small light bulb – the kind you would find in a torch

Two pieces of wire.

Method

1. Roll the piece of fruit on the table. Don't break the skin. Rolling it will get the juice flowing inside.

2. Stick the zinc nail into the fruit. Stick the copper nail 5cm away from the zinc nail. The two nails should not be touching. (Don't push the nails all the way through the fruit.)

3. Wrap a piece of wire around the zinc nail and attach this to one of the wires coming from the torch light bulb.

4. Wrap the other piece of wire around the copper nail and attach this to the other wire on the torch light bulb. The bulb will now come on!

Questions about the Story

What does Jilly think of Ben?

What does Ben think of Jilly?

What does Mr Jones think of Ben and Jilly?

Why doesn't Ben like Jilly's ideas for experiments?

What does Jilly imagine doing to Ben?

How did the things on Ben's list turn out to be useful?

How did Mr Z find out about the experiment?

How did Ben defeat Mr Z?

What happened to the gold grapefruit?

What did Mr Jones do at the end of the story, and why?